ARCHITECTURAL

CONTEMPORARY

ART GLASS STUDIOS

GLASS BY FISCHER

PUBLISHER: C&R LOO, INC.
1085 ESSEX AVENUE
RICHMOND, CALIFORNIA 94801 USA
PHONE: (510) 232-0276
FAX: (510) 232-7810

EDITOR: OLIVER LOO
CONTRIBUTING EDITOR: LIZ SHEEDY
FISCHER GLASS PHOTOGRAPHY: OLIVER LOO
GRAPHIC DESIGN: ZOOG DESIGN GROUP
TYPOGRAPHY: WOODWORTH TYPOGRAPHY
PRINTING: TREATY OAK PRESS

PHOTO CREDITS: ANDRÉ RAMJOUÉ 10, 11
JAMES M. LEWIS 16, 17
RICK MURAI 18
JANE LIDZ 19
CHERYL KOSKIE 31
STEVE SCHNEIDER 40
PABLO ESTEVA (MEXICO) 42, 43

ARCHITECTS: GEORGE (TAD) CODY 13
PATRICK J. KILLEN 14
MICHAEL LORIMER, K+CZL ASSOCIATES 19
J.C. MILNE 26
E. PAUL KELLY/JIM SAMUELS 29
EDUARDO DYER L. (MEXICO) 43

COVER PHOTO: FISCHER REAL ANTIQUE GLASS FA-345
BACK COVER PHOTO: FISCHER REAL ANTIQUE GLASS FA-426
TITLE PAGE PHOTO: FISCHER REAL ANTIQUE GLASS FA-344

LIBRARY OF CONGRESS CARD CATALOG NUMBER: 94-76586
COPYRIGHT © 1994 BY C&R LOO, INC.   ISBN 0-9641371-0-0

CONTENTS

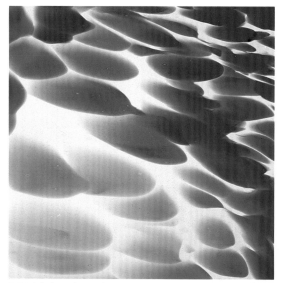

FA-314 *Dark Blue Patches on Amber*

THIS BOOK IS DEDICATED

TO THE GLASSBLOWERS AT

THE FISCHER GLASS FACTORY

AND TO THE ARTISTS

WHO USE FISCHER GLASS.

THROUGH THEIR SKILL

AND DEDICATION, THEY

CONTRIBUTE GIFTS OF ART

THAT CONTINUE TO INSPIRE

AND ENRICH OUR LIVES.

OLIVER LOO

FA-291 Pink and Blue on Clear, Streaky

INTRODUCTION

C&R LOO, Inc. was founded in 1973 by C.Y. and Rosemary Loo. In the beginning we imported A.C. Fischer Mouth-Blown Real Antique Glass and glass working tools and supplies to an enthusiastic and experimental group of artists. Through the years, we have watched this important group of artists flourish and grow. Our dedication to make available an extensive line of high quality materials for professional glass artists and designers has led to our ownership of the A.C. Fischer factory and our increased participation in the support of this art form.

The *Contemporary Architectural Art Glass Studios* book was developed to assist those who are interested in incorporating Art Glass in their lives and to document the current work of these artists who exemplify a contemporary approach to the ancient medium of stained glass. From architects to designers, builders, homeowners and those interested in the wondrous techniques of the stained glass art, this book is a valuable resource in discovering the rich and varied talents of these individuals who create custom glass work professionally.

We are pleased to introduce the following artists and their studios who we feel represent a vast array of beautiful quality work. The book encompasses a wide range of studios capable of providing an unlimited variety of custom glass designs, including architectural, ecclesiastical, and residential installations. The works pictured in this book are made using Fischer Real Antique Glass.

Please contact the studios directly to obtain information on commission work. Please do not let location deter you from considering the artists of your choice. As you will see by the list of selected commissions, most of the artists have installations out of state and overseas. If you would like to have more information on Fischer Glass or C&R LOO, please contact us at the address listed in the back of this book.

We hope that you enjoy this book and benefit from the information.

Thank you. C&R LOO, Inc.

DOUG SOELBERG

"Arrows #2"
Leaded Fischer Opak Glass
32" x 32"

Architectural Art Glass

410 W. 1200 N.

Orem, Utah 84057

(801) 224-6646

Fax (801) 223-9938

Selected Commissions

St. Patrick's Hospital, Missoula, MT

LDS Tabernacle, Provo, UT

St. Francis Catholic Church, Provo, UT

Markham Engineering, Provo, UT

St. Vincent de Paul Chapel, Salt Lake City, UT

Marie Callender's Restaurants, Orem, UT

Ibanez Corp., Whittier, CA

Architectural Art Glass has facilities and skill for working with acid and abrasive etching, glass slumping, and faceted glass, but most of their commissions are executed in lead and painted glass using mouth-blown Fischer Real Antique Glass. Architectural Art Glass has installed their work in churches, hospitals, and homes throughout the United States.

Doug Soelberg, as the owner of AAG, has been quietly producing window commissions and autonomous panels for nearly twenty years. He has tried to make sense of the great debate about the role of glass in architecture and has adopted the philosophy that "we're not just decorating buildings, but trying to create a culture." He hopes to achieve in his work a condition of stasis—where the viewer has to stop and contemplate the space. Soelberg's art pieces have won many awards and have been included in several international shows and exhibitions.

AAG is a studio experienced in the challenge of collaborative work with architects, designers, and other artists to create an architectural environment that is both aesthetically arresting and harmonious to the site. They are sensitive to the demands of the building process regarding scheduling and installation requirements.

Individual art work is represented by A.K.A. Skylight Gallery in Boston, MA, and Old Town Gallery, Park City, Utah.

"I Just Forgot"
Leaded Fischer Glass
Fired and Painted
32" x 42"

GORDON HUETHER

Codornui
34'' x 48''

Architectural Glass Design

101 South Coombs Street D

Napa, California 94559

(707) 255-5954

Fax (707) 255-5991

Selected Commissions

Stanford University Medical Center, Palo Alto, CA

Getty Museum Complex, Los Angeles, CA

Kaiser Permenente, Sacramento, CA

Church of Christ of Latter-Day Saints, American Fork, UT

Church of Christ of Latter-Day Saints, Hong Kong

San Diego Hospice, San Diego, CA

University of Alaska, Fairbanks, AK

Gordon Huether's artistic vision is to redefine the use of decorative glass in contemporary architecture. Resonant in Huether's work is the architect's conceptually pure language of forms. His designs convey the essential interdependence of environment and experience, of space and sensation. Huether's work connects the ancient medium of mouth-blown glass with state-of-the-art technologies. One way Huether bridges this gap is with his development of the patented glass technique known as INNER-LITE™.

INNER-LITE™ is an entirely new process of decorative glass for architectural applications. This revolutionary form of decorative glass marries the age old beauty of mouth-blown glass with the latest in commercial glazing technologies. The resulting union creates a new tool for manipulating light and color in today's architecture.

Huether's studio, Architectural Glass Design, was established in 1987. AGD operates in a 4,000 square foot facility which houses research and development, production and administration.

A separate 3,000 square foot facility provides space for the company's extensive design activities. The studio supports Huether's artistic vision and is proficient in all traditional decorative glass techniques and the production of INNER-LITE™.

Architects Huether has worked with include: Stone, Marraccini & Patterson; Richard Meier & Partners; Dreyfuss & Blackford Architects; IPA Architects; Seccombe Design Associates; and Carnum, Farnum, Igonda Interior Design.

UCSD Meditation Room
12' x 10'

JEFF G. SMITH

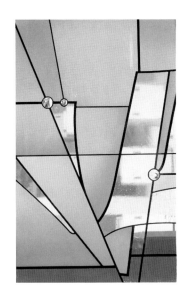

Library Window, Detail

Architectural Stained Glass, Inc.

P.O. Box 9092

Dallas, Texas 75209

(214) 352-5050

Fax (214) 827-5000

Selected Commissions

Worthen National Bank, Pine Bluff, AK

St. Alcuin Montessori School, Dallas, TX

Washington Hebrew Congregation, Washington, D.C.

University of Alaska, Fairbanks, AK

St. Mary Immaculate Church, Plainfield, IL

American Federal Bank, Dallas, TX

Wilcox Memorial Hospital, Lihue, HI

Chapel, Ellis II Max. Security Prison, Huntsville, TX

Since founding Architectural Stained Glass, Inc. in 1978, Jeff G. Smith has been creating stained glass that sensitively responds to a wide range of architectural environments. By not limiting himself exclusively to the two-dimensional picture-plane within a window, Smith's work is better able to explore the ever-changing and fully three-dimensional experiences stained glass can produce within an architectural space.

As he develops an empathy for the needs of those who will utilize a facility, Smith is also exploring the architectural concept, detailing and solar orientation of the actual structure. When melded with Smith's artistic talents, this thorough analysis results in a dynamically appropriate contribution to the overall architectural statement, and a more fulfilling experience for those who will use the space.

The Library window pictured to the right overlooks the library's atrium from the second floor stacks and reading area. The stained glass utilizes an achromatic palette of clear Fischer Real Antique Reamy, Crackle, Foam and Goethe juxtaposed with white Opal and Opak glass and clear lenses. The window draws color from its surrounding, while its imagery echoes the architectural light baffles in the atrium beyond. Light and shadow patterns projected from the atrium windows through these baffles add an exciting dimension to the adjacent spaces, as well as to the glass surface itself. This commission was sponsored by the Utah Arts Council.

Architectural Stained Glass provides a complete sequence of services from collaborative design through installation.

Library Window
Salt Lake City Community College, Utah
12.7' x 27.7'

Library Window, Detail

ARTHUR STERN

Portrait of the Artist
in the Apse Windows
Christ Church Episcopal

Arthur Stern Studios/Architectural Glass

1075 Jackson Street

Benicia, California 94920

(707) 745-8480

Selected Commissions

The new Federal Court House, Baton Rouge, LA

The Italian Cemetery Mausoleum Chapel, Colma, CA

The dome at City Center, Oakland, California

The Storrer House, Hollywood, CA

The Fawcett House, Los Banos, CA

LDS Mormon Temples, Bountiful, UT & Las Vegas, NV

St. Mary's Parish, Lakeport, CA

Arthur Stern Studios produces custom glass and wood detailing for architecture and interior design. The studio makes custom leaded glass windows, hardwood doors with leaded glass, room divider screens, and light fixtures. Color brochures are available on request.

"My work is primarily oriented towards architecture, adding art to the environment. Geometry is the language of architecture and it's a perfect vocabulary from which to design architectural glass detailing. Geometry is timeless.

"I try to design glass detailing that is sensitive to its environment, suitable to the function and scale of the building. I take hints from the architecture in choosing color, shape, and texture. The volumetric progressions, rhythms, proportions, and materials of the architecture help me focus my design intentions. Combining this with architects', designers', and clients' design criteria gives me a good departure point for designs.

"My work is a continuous process of exploring and refining a personal abstract language that I can apply to the specific criteria of an architectural project. I look forward to opportunities where good architecture and interior design are made better through the creative use of glass."

Arthur Stern Studios has installations all over the country with projects in twenty-four states.

Architects Stern has worked with include Post & Associates; Robert Overstreet; IDG Architects; Allen Erekson and Even Nielsen Architects; and several Frank Lloyd Wright projects.

"Frozen Music"
Leaded Fischer Antique Glass
with Beveled Glass Prisms
Christ Church Episcopal
60" x 60"

DENIS RICHARDSON

Waterwall Installation
8' x 24'

Catalina Glass Studio

2804 Dow Avenue

Redondo Beach, California 90278

Phone/Fax (310) 542-9220

Selected Commissions

Blake Edwards & Julie Andrews residence, Brentwood, CA

Billy Crystal residence, Pacific Palisades, CA

Melrose Place Fox TV, Santa Clarita TV Studios stageset

Mangiamo Ristorante, Manhattan Beach, CA

SportsCenter Bar & Grill, Redondo Beach, CA

Las Encinas Hospital, Pasadena, CA

Patrick J Killen, AIA, residence, Hermosa Beach, CA

Kaiser Permanente Hospital, Fontana, CA

Catalina Glass Studio is known for its commitment to artistic and technical excellence. Denis Richardson, principal designer with over twenty years experience working in collaboration with architects, interior designers, and decorators, produces compelling small and large scale projects. Successful installations of magnificent effects range from intimate portrait panels to window walls, entry doors, room dividers and light screens which are fully integrated with the forms and purpose of the architecture.

These architectonic constructions, sometimes layered, incorporate the highest quality materials including A.C. Fischer Real Antique Glass that vitalize interior spaces with a balanced and optimum light transmission. Whether the space is private or public, Catalina Glass Studio is noted for its dedication to thoughtful, elegant, architecturally integrated art.

Catalina Glass Studio provides full service, from initial conceptual consultation with computer generated design presentations and maquettes to construction and installation. Architects and designers concerned with compatibility are encouraged to collaborate on projects requiring high quality design aesthetics.

A portfolio slide presentation, available by appointment, will further demonstrate recent project's architectural relationship and acquaint you with design techniques and materials.

Individual projects are quoted with consideration to design requirements.

Ernst Residence
Leaded Fischer Opals
and Geveled Green Glass

RUSSELL J. TROWBRIDGE

Geometric Design
36" x 24"

Diameter Artglass

P.O. Box 2373

Nevada City, California 95959

(916) 478-1124

Selected Commissions

1930 Model A Ford, Ratzlaff Ford-Mercury, Visalia, CA

Germination, Private Collection, Sacramento, CA

Pureblo Sunrise, Private Collection, Nevada City, CA

Russell Trowbridge experimented with an approach he labels "three-dimensional realism" in Art Glass in the mid 1970's in Carmel, California, where he collaborated with glass designer John A. Crum to create a strong direction in his Art Glass. Using ever-popular stained glass themes: birds in flight, sailing ships at sea, and eventually the classic automobile, Russell strives to create the illusion of depth in his work.

Classic cars became the popular interest of his Carmel clients.

Currently residing in the historical art community of Nevada City, California, Russell Trowbridge is working on a revival of interest in the "American love affair" with classic automobiles. He has the distinction of being one of a few glass artists specializing in these renditions that he terms "three-dimensional realism."

Techniques of glass layering and sculpture soldering are enhanced by the unique qualities of A.C. Fischer's flashed colors. These techniques combine to create an image that expands out of the plane of the frame.

Russell Trowbridge's works are available in hardwood frames custom made by the artist.

1928 Duesenberg
40'' x 27''

ELIZABETH DEVEREAUX

Sunnyvale Public Library
12' x 21'

**Elizabeth Devereaux
Architectural Glass**

2155B Park Avenue
Chico, California 95928
Phone/Fax (916) 342-2074

Selected Commissions

Mercy Hospital Chapel, Bakersfield, CA
St. Peter's Catholic Church, Monument, CO
Our Lady of the Hills Catholic Church, Columbia, SC
Newman Center, University of Missouri, Columbia, MO
Sunnyvale Public Library, Sunnyvale, CA
Sacramento Public Library, Sacramento, CA

Philosophizing about my 25 years as a stained glass artist, I realize that my work is deeply reflective in two ways—both in meaning and in use of materials.

My process for all projects involves three interactive factors EVALUATION of all project issues—the client's intent, the location and environment, the light, the architecture. COLLABORATION with the client, committee and architect. DESIGN collaboratively from preliminary to finished designs.

With formal training in painting and drawing in the U.S. and Europe, my work often integrates elements of antiquity with the new, both in material and design. It is further influenced by my love of nature, my strong interest in architecture and theology, by artists

Nolde, Klee, Redon, O'Keefe, Clemente, and architects—Adolph Loos, Johann Hoffman, Otto Wagner, Greene & Greene, Le Corbusier, Hans Hollein, and Chris Alexander.

Graduate studies in industrial design lead me to explore various materials and techniques in search of the right sympathy between glass and architecture. My father often quoted John Gardner's book, *Excellence,* and that attitude underlies all the work my staff and I produce.

The Sunnyvale Public Library, pictured above, has a peaceful landscape view out of the East Wing window; I chose to use it as part of the design. The theme "the library as the center of learning in the community" was em-

bodied in the mountains, symbolizing lofty pursuit and achievement, the river—the riches of knowledge flowing into the foreground—to humankind, receivers of those riches. The "brick" border design repeats the entry detail throughout the building.

The challenge of St. Joseph's Cathedral, pictured at the right, was to design three new windows to be integrated into the 115 year old state and national landmark with the existing windows, architecture and geometry. I distilled the original window composition into a painted architectural border, a gold Greek cross motif middle ground (reflecting the floor plan) and a central "figure"—interior windows depicting themes of baptism, resurrection, and eucharist.

St. Joseph's Cathedral
14.5' x 4.5' Each

GÜNTER GROHS

Glass Divider Wall
Private Residence

**Glasgestaltungen–
Günter Grohs**

Friederichstraße 119 A
38855 Wernigerode
Germany
Phone 3943-32208

Selected Commissions

St. Laurentius Church, Nienstedt, Germany

Wilhelm-Raabe School, Wernigerode, Germany

Retirement home "An der Oesig," Blankenburh, Germany

Private residence, Wernigerode, Germany

Promenade Hotel, Friedrichsbrunn, Germany

Chamber of Commerce, Wernigerode, Germany

Günter Grohs graduated from the Academy of Art and Design in Halle, Germany in the late 80's. He has since opened his own studio in Wernigerode, Germany. He prefers working with two or three colors, stating that "the eye needs a resting place in a world of so many influences." He likes to use as few lead lines as possible, preferring instead to let the color of the glass and the sandblasted areas of the flashed glass determine the design. The situation in East Germany prior to reunification led him to experiment widely with different glass and glass techniques. Grohs sees the function of glass as a "light filter," a filter that does not obscure the view to the outside world around us.

He has numerous public, private and corporate installations throughout Germany. His works have received many national and international awards.

St. Michael Church
Völkershausen, Germany

THOMAS HÖLZER

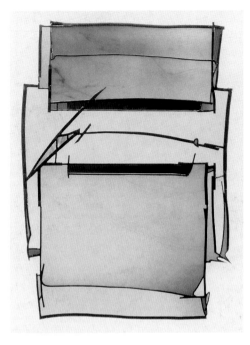

"Expo '94 #1"
34" x 25"

Glass Design Studios
P.O. Box 2278
Boulder, Colorado 80306-2278
(303) 449-2085
Fax (303) 449-8745

Selected Commissions
Boulder Community Hospital, Boulder, CO
Kaiser Permanente Foundation, Longmont, CO
Utah Arts Council, UT
Teachers Insurance & Annuity Association, NY
United Church of Christ, Broomfield, CO
Gary, Naegele & Theado, Lorain, OH
Patti & Dimitri Colevas-Allen, Cambridge, MA
Grim Danese, Oslo, Norway
Dr. Laura & Dr. Buddy Thomason, Denver, CO
Warren Miller, Boulder, CO

Thomas Hölzer formulates designs which are derived from his imagination, the environment and his two decades of exposure to the medium of Art Glass. When creating, conceptual lines and shapes are captured in charcoal drawings and color sketches. When initial ideas are finalized, they explode on a canvas of mouth-blown glass.

The essence of his design approach is retained when working on large scale architectural projects. Commissions and collaborations are researched in painstaking detail to ensure an uninhibited flow of creativity during the design process. By combining this innovative artistic approach with exacting technical expertise, the opportunity to produce exclusive, custom designed Art Glass and mosaic with high aesthetic sensibility is unlimited.

Wall Divider and Window Treatment
Charles T. Wallace Residence
Boulder, Colorado

JANE MARQUIS

Private Residence Window
Claremont, California

Jane Marquis Stained Glass

1038 Alamosa Drive

Claremont, California 91711

(909) 624-8368

Selected Commissions

Temple Rodef Sholem, San Rafael, California

Oviatt Building, Los Angeles, CA

St. Matthew's Parish, Pacific Palisades, CA

All Souls Episcopal Church, Berkeley, CA

Science Library at the University of Oregon

Church of the Nativity, Rancho Santa Fe, CA

Robert Sowers wrote: "The appearance of a stained glass window is always radically affected by whatever is actually *there* in the overall luminous environment of which it is a part. Change any element of that luminous environment, whether it be the position of the sun and clouds, or the light transmitting qualities of an adjacent window, and you change the effect of the whole. The myth that the radiance of the old windows is somehow inherent in the glass itself, the product of some wondrous lost glass coloring technique, is simply the persistent mechanical bias of a grossly mechanical civilization."

"As a stained glass artist I must know a site as intimately as possible beforehand, mostly with time spent looking, then through sketches, photographs and trial panels. This way I hope to create the 'overall luminous environment' that Mr. Sowers so eloquently describes. A transformation of the quality of light from a window to a wall."

Jane Marquis has numerous commissions for private residences in California and elsewhere.

Baptistery, St. Matthew's Parish
Pacific Palisades, California

JEAN MYERS

Cherokee Memorial Park
Mausoleum Chapel
Lodi, California

Jean Myers Architectural Glass
P.O. Box 17188
South Lake Tahoe, California 96151
Phone/Fax (916) 541-7878

Selected Commissions
Fuqua Industries Executive Office, Atlanta, GA
Sutter General Hospital, Sacramento, CA
First Christian Church, Portland, OR
Christ the King Catholic Community church, Las Vegas, NV
Our Saviour's United Methodist Church, Schaumburg, IL
Cherokee Memorial Park, Lodi, CA

Jean Myers works nationally as an architectural art designer. She works primarily in leaded glass, but has done projects in carved glass, marble and glass mosaics, and carved brick. Myers uses the multiple functions of Art Glass as fine art which can control the intensity and color of light in a setting or enhance a view or shields one that is unpleasant.

She creates art which embodies the expression and needs of her clients and becomes a part of the architectural set-ting. Myers designs from abstract to symbolic forms in a limited palette of color, striving for flow and simplicity. She creates environments that treasure tranquility and strength for those who will live a portion of their lives within the space.

Architects Myers has worked with include: Henningson, Durham and Richardson Architects; Pecsok, Jelliffe, Randall Architects; G.C. Wallace, Inc. Architects; Cone, Kalb, Wonderlick Architects; J.C. Milne.

Resurrection Windows
Christ the King Catholic
Community Church
Las Vegas, Nevada
5.5' x 12'

SHELLEY JURS

Double Door
Fischer Reamy, Transparent colors
and Hand Cast Jewels
6' x 8'

Jurs Architectural Glass

4167 Wilshire Blvd.

Oakland, California 94602

Phone Studio (510) 521-7765

Phone Office (510) 482-0225

Fax (510) 531-6173

Selected Commissions

Oceanside Civic Center, Oceanside, CA

Kaiser Medical Facility Lobby, Napa, CA

Kaiser Medical Facility Lobby, San Francisco, CA

Civic Center, Pleasant Hill, CA

Library, Redwood City, CA

Larkspur Library, Larkspur, CA

Integrating Art + Architecture, Jurs award winning one of a kind, custom leaded glass designs are fabricated with mouth-blown and hand cast glasses imported from Germany. Works can be installed into wood or metal framing systems for grand entrances, window walls, skylights, domes, and atriums for site-specific residential and commercial design environments. Jurs Architectural Glass has installed works nationally and internationally for over a decade.

Elaborate design models are provided for each project.

Architects Jurs has worked with include: Charles Moore/Urban Innovations Group; E. Paul Kelly AIA/Jim Samuels;Hospital Designers Inc./ Mark Sennette Interior Designer; Fisher Freidman Associates/Charles Moore; Bull Stockwell, Allen & Ripley; Swanson & Associates.

A free catalogue of our work is available. By appointment only.

Kaiser Permanente Hospital
Napa, California

LEONE McNEIL

Autonomous Panel
24" x 30"

Lead and Light Works

P.O. Box 552

Mendocino, California 95460

Phone/Fax (707) 937-5227

Selected Commissions

Fort Bragg Presbyterian Church, Fort Bragg, CA

Mendocino Presbyterian Church, Mendocino, CA

Trinity Lutheran Church, Fort Bragg, CA

Kelsyville Presbyterian Church, Kelsyville, CA

Leone McNeil's early training was as an Art Major at U.C.L.A. in Southern California where she earned a B.E. degree in art.

After raising three children, she attended a four year program at Otis Art Institute, Los Angeles, California. There she received her B.A. and a M.F.A. degree in Fine Arts with a thesis project having been done in fused glass.

During the past sixteen years, McNeil has continued her studies in glass at Pilchuck and through workshops with Ludwig Schaffrath, Johannes Schreiter, Patrick Reyntiens, Brian Clarke and the late Roger Darricarrere as well as traveling extensively in many parts of the world, focusing on art in general and stained glass in particular.

Leone is a member of the Stained Glass Association of America, Interfaith Forum for Religious Art and Architecture, and the Art Glass Suppliers Association.

McNeil's initial interest was doing secular works in glass, principally non-figurative in style. Later pieces have been religious and both figurative as well as non-figurative. Clearly there is a sympathetic feeling for the spiritual aspect of religious works.

Art for her is a continually growing process which her life also exemplifies. Living and working in Mendocino, a small artists' community in Northern California, has given her opportunities for a more reflective pattern of life and a changing set of values which seem to bring things into a perspective of balance apparent in her work.

Hoag Memorial
Presbyterian Hospital
9.5' x 6'

LESLIE PERLIS

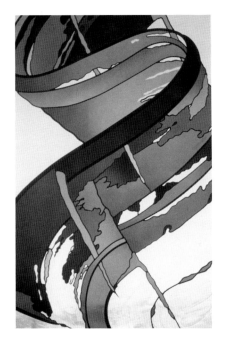

"Chromatic Current"
30" x 44"

Leslie Perlis Studio

San Diego, California

(619) 222-8776

Fax (619) 224-0587

Selected Commissions

Temple Solel, Encinitas, CA

Seacrest Chapel, Encinitas, CA

Temple Adat Shalom, Rancho Bernardo, CA

Tiffereth Israel Synagogue, San Diego, CA

Leslie Perlis, a pioneer in the Art Glass field, discovered glass as a form of artistic expression in 1971. Since then she has created many commissions for residential, commercial and religious installations. Leslie creates cutting edge designs which are a collaboration between the needs of the client, the architectural setting and her artistic talents.

Over the years she has developed her own original and unique style, striving to give stained glass a future beyond the design trends of the past. Her current work is a visual interpretation of the unforeseen forces in our lives. It depicts phenomenon that we all feel and know exist, like natural and spiritual energy and the power of color. Her abstract design approach allows for individual interpretation of her work.

Perlis's award winning stained glass, fused glass and anodized titanium pieces have been exhibited and published internationally. She will continue her innovative vision while bringing her glasswork into the future, creating glass art that is light years ahead.

The "Wavelength" stained glass window was commissioned for a private residence. The design depicts the power of water and the comforting effect it has on us, in this appropriate location over a master bath tub. Fabrication by Heather Trimlett.

The "Chromatic Current" exhibition piece illustrates the flow of color throughout our lives. It appeared on the cover of *Glass Art Magazine* (Jan/Feb 1993), and won first place honors in the "Art in All Media Show" for Perlis and her fabricator Heather Trimlett.

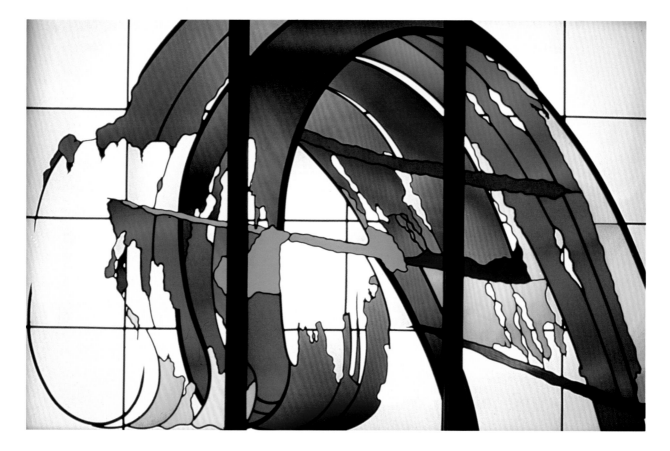

"Wavelength"

4' x 6'

LUTZ HAUFSCHILD

"Glimpse of the Garden of Earthly Delights"
Etched and Leaded Antique Glass
43" x 43"

Lutz Haufschild

1461 Nelson Avenue

West Vancouver, B.C. V7T 2G9

Canada

(604) 926-8594

Fax (604) 926-9452

Selected Commissions

Westminster Abbey, Mission, British Columbia, CAN

Robson Court, Vancouver, British Columbia, CAN

Thurston High School, Olympia, WA

Burnaby Mosque, Burnaby, British Columbia, CAN

Telesat Headquarters, Ottawa, Ontario, CAN

Skydome Stadium, Toronto, Ontario, CAN

Ontario Crafts Council, Toronto, Ontario, CAN

East 21 Hotel, Tokyo, Japan

Lutz Haufschild has completed over 200 projects internationally. He consults at length with architects, art consultants, designers and developers before he starts the design process. His artistic response to architectural givens is either bold, with strong but harmonious colors; or restrained, creating a timeless elegance with clear glass, bevels and prisms. The resulting glass projects are more often than not unusual, but are always appropriate, in order to arrive at a convincing integration of art and architecture.

"Trinity Windows"
St. Andrews Lutheran Church
Etched and Leaded Antique Glass

LYN HOWE

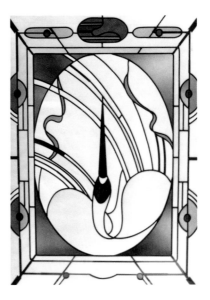

Skylight
Leaded Fischer Opal and Flashed Antique Glass
32" x 44"

Lyn Howe Architectural Glass Design

5753 Landregen Street

Emeryville, California 94608

(510) 601-0107

Fax (510) 601-1015

Selected Commissions

Ridgeview Commons Library, Pleasanton, CA

New Providence Baptist Church, San Francisco, CA

Bank Planning Associates, Sausalito, CA

Arthur E. Guedel Memorial Anestisia Ctr., San Francisco, CA

Pacific Latin American Church, La Puente, CA

Glendale Federal Savings, San Mateo, CA

The Philip K. Burton Federal Building, San Francisco, CA

Lyn Howe Architectural Glass Design specializes in the design and fabrication of innovative glass art work for commercial and residential installations. From a stained glass screen that recreates the colors and textures of an African Kente cloth to a series of panels that incorporate stained and leaded glass, painted and fired glass and fused glass, the studio's work is diverse and creative, sensitive to color, materials, function, shape and scale. Lyn Howe's studio is recognized for excellence in fabrication, knowledge of technical re-

quirements, and understanding of architectural and design movements from past to present.

A wide range of fabrication techniques is offered by Lyn Howe Architectural Glass Design, enabling the client to choose one technique or to incorporate several to suit the design requirements of the project. Fabrication techniques include sandblasted and sandcarved glass; leaded glass, stained and beveled; copper foil glass; etched mouth-blown flashed glass; fused glass; kiln-slumped glass; glue chipped glass;

kiln fired painted glass surfaces; and airbrushed painted surfaces.

Lyn Howe has more than 17 years of experience in the glass industry. She began working with glass at Anderson Windows as the manager of the extrusion and formulation lab. In 1984, She started as an associate at Bruce McLean Studio, became operating partner in 1987, and operating owner of Lyn Howe Architectural Glass Design, formerly Bruce McLean Studio, in 1989.

Untitled
Leaded Fischer Transparent Antique Glass
37'' x 57''

MARGARET NELSON

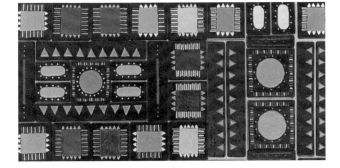

"Glass Tile Splashback"
36' x 20'

Margaret Nelson Studio

P.O. Box 22

Tesuque, New Mexico 87574

(505) 988-1762

Selected Commissions

Cypress Creek Cafe, Wimberely, TX

Ishpiming Educational Center, WI

Private residence, awarded by *Texas Architect,* Santa Fe, NM

Private residence, Minneapolis, MN

Design capabilities that range from the outrageous to the sublime, whatever the client wishes to explore...

"I believe in the magic that emerges from the close interplay with designer, client and artist, and I believe in the magic of light passing through beautifully wrought glass."

Margaret Nelson's studio is situated in the creatively energetic sphere of Santa Fe, New Mexico, where her work results in a blend of fresh ideas burnished by enduring tradition. Here, the enchantment of the land quickens the artist's heart and hand.

Her work is found throughout the country, in commercial installations and private collections.

She also produces a unique series of window design, lighting, glass tiles, mirrors, and sandetched glass.

"Ishpiming"
3' x 6'

MICHAEL F. PILLA

Entry Door
Steel and Glass with Copper Cames
Collaboration with Irve Dell, Sculptor

Monarch Studios, Inc.

2242 University Ave., Suite 316

St. Paul, Minnesota 55114

(612) 644-7927

Fax (612) 649-0456

Selected Commissions

Moorehead State University, Moorehead, MN

Minnesota Judicial Buildings, St. Paul, MN

Chubb Insurance Co., Hartford, CT

University of Notre Dame, South Bend, IN

Temple of ECK, Chanhassen, MN

Atwater residence, Telluride, CO

Michael F. Pilla, through Monarch Studios, Inc., provides original design in architectural art glass for private and commercial clients. The design work is most often created for execution utilizing copper cames and an original fabrication technique. However, he also uses lead cames when it is deemed most appropriate. He often collaborates with other artists, designers and architects and he enjoys the opportunities and challenges that these collaborative efforts bring.

Pilla has evolved a strong personal aesthetic and execution of all designs is completed in-house to ensure that this aesthetic is maintained.

"My work has been strongly influenced by the artist/craftsman ideals of the American Arts and Crafts tradition, in that a hands-on involvement with materials and techniques is particularly important in my process of creation. I strive to keep alive the rich tradition of American glass working by producing forms which are rooted in the past, but are fitting for a contemporary architectural environment. At the same time my work is driven by a love of these materials I employ, a historical understanding of the craft, and a belief in the continually evolving possibilities of the medium due, in part, to the ever-increasing availability of new technologies."

"I place a great deal of importance on the degree of detail and finish I bring to my pieces, not as an end in itself, but rather as another aspect of the design to be appreciated by the viewer."

Michael Pilla founded Monarch Studios in 1976, and it has been operation in St. Paul, Minnesota since January of that year.

Autonomous Panel
Fischer Real Antique Glass
and Lead Cames
32' x 42'

BERT GLAUNER

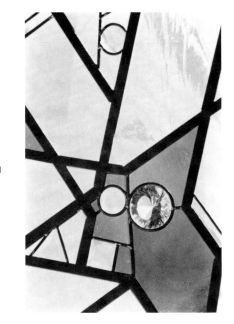

"Espiral" Detail

Morelia Glass Design Center

Apartado Postal 670

58000 Morelia, Michoacan

Mexico

Phone/Fax 52-43-140063

Selected Commissions

Hotel San Cayetano, Zitacuaro, Michoacan, MEX

Catholic Church "Corazon de Marie," Morelia, Michoacan, MEX

Offices, Grupo CAIL, Polanco, Mexico City, MEX

Private residence, Fuenterrabia, Spain

Office building, Morelia, Michoacan, MEX

Private residence, CEO Banca Serfin, Mexico City, MEX

The Morelia Glass Design Center is a modern glass studio located in Morelia, Michoacan, about three hours by car from Mexico City.

Under the supervision of owner/ artist Bert Glauner, who studied painting and jewelry design at the *"Kunst-und Werkschule"* in Pforzheim, Germany, the studio specializes in abstract designs of panels, windows, and other architectonic installations.

The creative work of Bert Glauner offers solutions for design problems in architecture; fabrication and installation are executed according to highest standards by the studio.

The artist encourages a close collaboration during the design process with the client, architect and/or interior designer, a cooperation that should exist in order to achieve best results. Bert Glauner sees his creations as an integral part of the tectonic space; a symbiosis between space and light, enhanced and modulated by glass.

Bert Glauner, through the Morelia Glass Design Center, has executed numerous commissions in Mexico, U.S.A. and Spain; his work has been installed in churches, private residences and corporate office buildings.

His autonomous, non-commissioned art in stained glass and sculpture have been shown in exhibitions in galleries and museums.

The Morelia Glass Design Center, besides fabricating Bert Glauner's designs, also organizes workshops and seminars and has presented internationally renowned artists such as Dan Fenton, Lutz Haufschild, Eric Hilton, and Jochem Poensgen.

"Espiral"
 Private residence skylight
 16' x 16'

PATTIE WALKER

Metropolitan Toronto City Hall

Pattie Walker Studio

290 Carlaw Avenue Unit 203

Toronto, Ontario M4M 3L1

Canada

Phone/Fax (416) 465-8249

Selected Commissions

Enterprise Property Group, Toronto, Ontario, CAN

Private residence, Toronto, Ontario, CAN

Metropolitan Toronto City Hall Protocol Room, Toronto, Ontario, CAN

Christ Church, Ridgewood, NJ

St. Bartholomew's, Toronto, Ontario, CAN

From a background in classical glass, my work has evolved into a significant exploration of glass appliqué. Appliqué offers a versatility that is different from traditional leaded work. While equally rigorous in its execution, there is a spontaneity and freedom in the composition of the image. It is a painterly approach—you can add a spot of color or texture here and there, create depth by overlaying colors and shapes, or emphasize a line or shape by the addition or subtraction of an element.

Unlike leaded glass, which must be back-lit for maximum effect, appliqué can work with ambient light. The absence of lead and the presence of resin operate together to enhance the light-bearing capacity of the glass. This allows the exploration of form; an exploration that can move in a sculptural direction. Free standing pieces can be combined, arranged, and overlapped three dimensionally.

In the photo above, two thematic elements were overlaid to create the translucent interior walls. Abstracted views of Toronto's main river systems and topography were sandblasted on one sheet of plate glass. The historical divisions of Metro Toronto election wards provided the shapes for the second sheet of plate. The two sheets of plate were glazed together in a metal framework, separated by a spacer.

For me, art is about making contact. Commission work and public art challenges the artist to collaborate with the client in representing a vision. This vision must be a marriage between the artist's creative integrity and the architectural and community contexts.

I have been working in glass since 1981. My architectural commissions include projects for residential, commercial and liturgical installations. I use a variety of techniques including the more traditional painted, etched and leaded stained glass, as well as sandblasting and glass appliqué/mosaic.

Metropolitan Toronto City Hall
Protocol Room
9' x 38'

DAVID & MICHELLE PLACHTE-ZUIEBACK

"Fourth Day of Creation: Wheels of Time"
18" x 40"

Plachte-Zuieback Art Glass

1445 Carlos Court

Santa Rosa, California 95409

(707) 539-8220

Selected Commissions

Temple Emanu-El, San Diego, CA

Anton residence, Santa Rosa, CA

Temple Beth Sholom, San Leandro, CA

AIDS/HIV Life Center, San Francisco, CA

Golob residence, Malibu, CA

First Assembly of God, Willits, CA

Willits City Hall, Willits, CA

Plachte-Zuieback Art Glass provides highly original designs for stained glass windows for residential and public buildings, churches and synagogues. We create windows which reflect and enhance the architectural setting, while expressing a meaningful aesthetic which goes beyond the mere decoration. Our windows have content. Our designs encourage the viewer to reflect. Through our work, we make statements, draw conclusions, shed new light. Our work provokes thought, inspires interest and challenges tradition.

We design and fabricate our own work to architectural specifications, incorporating techniques which, in addition to traditional lead work include sandblast etching, glass fusing, glass painting, lamination and sandblast carving on clear plate glass for use in doors, free-standing screens and windows.

Also, our team of experienced professionals provide complete installation services for our work, including co-ordination with commercial glaziers for thermo-paning, tempering and laminated float glass applications.

On request, we prepare proposals which include designs to scale, timetables and complete budgets. We enjoy working with people, are experienced at working with committees and are available for discussions of all aspects of our work.

"It Is a Tree of Life"
Temple Valley Beth Shalom
35' x 20'

NARCISSUS QUAGLIATA

Private Residence Door
Leaded Fischer Glass with Mouth-Blown
Rondels and Custom Made Bevels
21" x 60"

Quagliata Studios

1520 Third Street

Oakland, California 94607

(510) 452-4327

Fax (510) 839-9579

Selected Commissions

Blue Cross headquarters, Oakland, CA

Screen Actors Guild Business Arts Plaza Building, Burbank, CA

National Advanced Systems, Santa Clara, CA

The Alice Arts Center, Oakland, CA

Yerba Buena Parking Facility, San Francisco, CA

Narcissus Quagliata custom designs very contemporary works in glass for residential and commercial interiors. Quagliata incorporates A. C. Fischer Real Antique and sandblasted glass with custom bevels and metal to achieve designs which can be illuminated by natural or artificial lighting.

With many years of experience collaborating with designers, Quagliata's studio has created work, both small and monumental, for interiors across the U.S., Europe, and Mexico.

Private Residence
Leaded Fischer Glass with Mouth-Blown
Rondels and Custom Made Bevels
9' x 12'

CLAIRE M. WING

"Guarding Angels"

Wing Glass Works

1520 W. Ninth Street

Dallas, Texas 75208

Phone/Fax (214) 761-9464

Selected Commissions

Schumpert Medical Center, Shreveport, LA

St. Rita Catholic Commmunity, Dallas, TX

Montserrat Jesuit Retreat House, Lake Dallas, TX

Prestonwood Baptist Chruch, Dallas, TX

Dallas/Fort Worth Airport Chapel Terminal, TX

Religious of Mary Immaculate, San Antonio, TX

St. Mark's School of Texas, Dallas, TX

Scofield Memorial Church, Dallas, TX

When a client commissions a work in glass, particularly a large work for their place of worship or health care facility, they have confidence that the artist will produce a work of beauty. Deeper still, I believe, is an often unspoken hope that something beyond good design alone would be evident. That some spiritual atmosphere, some feeling would prevail, something that reaches beyond an intellectual connection to touch us inwardly.

Along side the budgetary concerns and thematic interests of the client, the integrity and intent of the surrounding architecture, and discussions over materials, colors or techniques, the guiding force behind of all these important elements is still what the client hopes to feel once they are standing in the space.

My work includes examples of architectural leaded glass, carved glass murals, monumental glass sculpture, and other works that provide solutions to out of the ordinary architectural settings. Early involvement in the project can help me assist in setting an appropriate budget, address technical questions and develop schedules that coordinate with other project activities. There is always a way to create art which speaks to people within any budget.

"Those Who Mourn"
St. Luke's Catholic Church
Irving, Texas

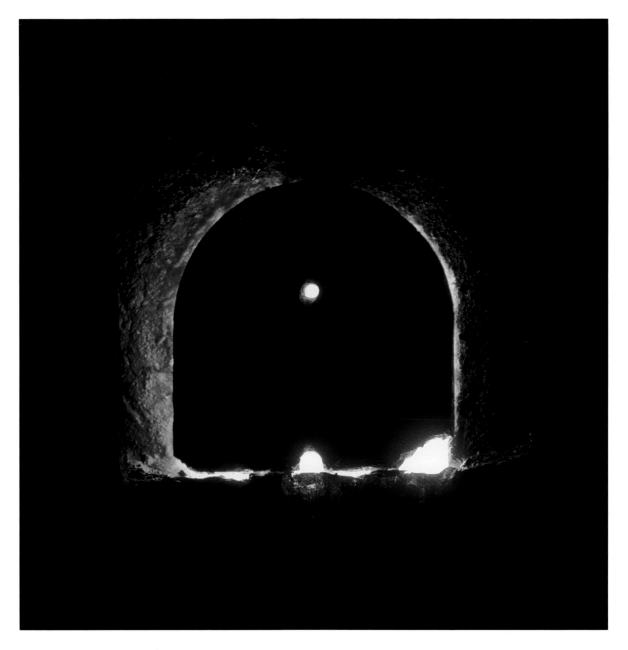

Glass Furnace at 2400°F

FISCHER REAL ANTIQUE GLASS

Fischer Real Antique Glass is made by combining the same traditional methods of making glass used almost eight centuries ago with the best of modern technology. Each sheet of Fischer Glass contains provocative elements of color, textural and compositional variations, which are seen only in Real Antique Glass. Fischer Real Antique Glass is made entirely by hand. In contrast to machine made glass, which is formed by metal rollers which force the glass into the desired shape and thickness, Fischer Real Antique Glass is formed entirely by the skill of the master glassblower. This mouth-blown process gives Fischer Glass a unique optical quality and depth of color that other processes can not match.

A.C. Fischer manufactures over 500 different standard colors, each available in a certain combination of color, texture, flash, shading, translucency and transparency. In addition to the 500 standard colors, A.C. Fischer can produce any one of several thousand different other colors, or combinations of colors, textures, shadings and activity. With its many distinctive surface appearances, colors, and types of glass, Fischer Real Antique Glass is the finest glass available for the stained glass, architectural and decorative arts.

FISCHER GLASS TECHNIQUE

To make glass, sand, soda and limestone are melted in large crucibles. Various metal oxides are then added to color the glass. When the glass is sufficiently melted, the master glassblower gathers a small amount of glass at the end of a blowpipe. The blowpipe is then slowly turned and the glass is carefully worked to form a molten, spherical bubble. The bubble is then elongated to form a cylinder. Striations (lines in the surface of the glass) are then applied while the cylinder is still hot. Next, the end of the cylinder is opened and the cylinder is separated from the blowpipe. The cylinder is then placed in an annealing oven where it is allowed to cool slowly. After the cylinder has cooled sufficiently, it is cut open, reheated in another oven, opened and flattened out. The resulting sheet is approximately 24" wide by 36" tall, with a thickness of about ⅛".

FISCHER GLASS TYPES

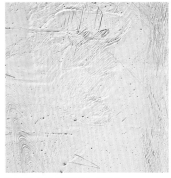
FA-Goethe Clear, No Striations, No Seeds

GOETHE GLASS

Goethe glass is "Old style mouth-blown glass." It is a clear Real Antique Glass with no seeds or striation lines. The subtle texture one sees in the glass results from the natural distortion of the free blown process.

FA-53R Clear Reamy

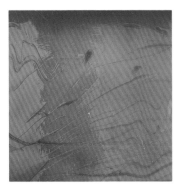
FA-122R Amber Reamy

REAMY

Reamy glass is a Real Antique Glass with a distinctive wavy, drapery-like surface. It sometimes has large, irregular, round or oval "ox-eyes" on the surface of the glass formed from flattened bubbles. Reamy glass has a folded, water-like quality that imparts the illusion of motion. This dynamic glass is available in clear, transparent, opak and flashed colors that range from quiet and subtle to dramatic and active. Its brilliant refractive and reflecting qualities can obscure views and provide a sense of privacy.

FA-Foam Clear, Striations, Heavy Foamy Seeds

SEEDY CLEARS

Fischer produces four types of clear seeded glass each containing different concentrations of seed bubbles. They range from lightly seeded sheets with only a few bubbles interspersed throughout, to heavily seeded sheets in which the bubbles are tightly packed within the glass where they create a "foamy" appearance.

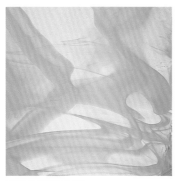

FA-426 Opal White on Clear

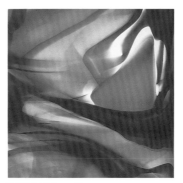

FA-404 Cobalt Blue on Clear

CONTINENTAL STREAKY

Continental Streakies are transparent on transparent streakies. Opal is not used in this glass, with the exception of a white and clear Continental Streaky. These streakies have a very soft, water-color like effect. This effect is similar to that of moving a paint brush over a water saturated paper—the color will bleed out into the paper in some areas, and in others it remains where it was put. The shading in the Continental Streakies is gradual and the colors are diffuse.

FA-369 Ruby Red on Selenium Yellow

FLASHED GLASS

Flashed glass is composed of one (single) or two (double) thin (flashed) layers of a darker color on a clear or light colored base glass. Because of the thin flash layer, the appearance of a sheet can vary from an even and uniform appearance, to a subtle gradation from light to dark, to an abrupt and dramatic interruption of color.

When two different colors are flashed together, a rich third color results. An example is a red on selenium yellow glass (pictured left), in which the changing thickness of the red flash creates a shaded orange color with the yellow below. Another example is a cobalt blue on medium green glass (pictured left), in which the shaded areas create a turquoise color.

The variations of flashed glass add a dimension to the stained glass palette that is both subtle and striking. Through the careful use of the light and dark areas within a sheet of flashed glass, a rich spatial sense can be achieved. Flashed glass is often used for acid etching and sandblasting. These processes create graphic designs by selectively etching away the flashed layer to reveal the contrasting base below.

FA-364 Cobalt Blue on Green

FISCHER GLASS TYPES

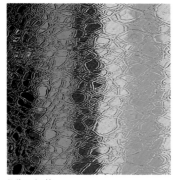

FA-Clear Crackle

CRACKLE

Crackle glass is a Real Antique Glass that has an alligator skin pattern. Crackle glass distorts views more completely than does Reamy glass. It is available in a range of clear and transparent colors. The intense light breaking quality seen in crackle allows light to sparkle through, while still maintaining privacy.

FA-119 Medium Brown

FA-78 Cobalt Blue

TRANSPARENT COLORS

Fischer Transparent glass is available in a wide variety of colors and textures. The palette ranges from intensely vibrant primary and secondary colors, to quiet and subtle pastel and grayed colors. Each color is available in many tonal variations. Transparent colors are ideal for enhancing a view and are most effectively used when back lighting is available to bring out their rich, vibrant colors.

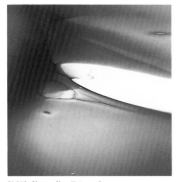

FA-161 Blue on Clear Variegated

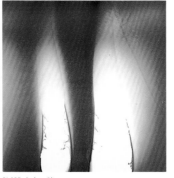

FA-157 Red on Blue

VARIEGATED GLASS

When the flashed layer is manipulated by the glassblower so that it is quite thick in some areas and fades out completely in other areas, a variegated glass results. These variegated sheets may be transparent on transparent, opal on transparent, or opal on color. Variegated glass will have some areas of smooth gradation and other areas in which change is so abrupt and complete that a dramatic line occurs. These lines are sometimes used to extend other lines and leading in a design.

FA-319 Selenium Yellow Opak

OPAL AND OPAK

Opal glass has a thin layer of white opal flashed on one side of a clear or colored base glass. This "flash" gives the sheet a semi-transparent or veiled appearance. Opak is similar to Opal, except that the white Opak glass is denser, producing a translucent, but non-transparent sheet of glass. When looking through a sheet of Opal glass, outlines of objects and light and dark areas are discernable. A sheet of Opak glass on the other hand, will reveal only its color and shading, while nothing beyond can be seen.

The thin flash of white on both Opal or Opak sheets allows this glass to reveal its color without back lighting, unlike transparent glass. This ability to hold their color even in poorly lit spaces is especially useful to artists and designers when dealing with such spaces.

Opal and Opak glass can be used to soften the harsh qualities of direct sunlight. When used in combination with transparent colors, the illusion of depth can be created with the Opals and Opaks as "figure" and the transparents as "ground."

FA-64 Opal White on Clear

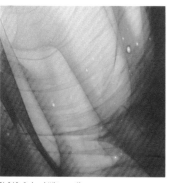
FA-345 Red and White on Clear

FA-355 Blue on Rose Streaky

FISCHER STREAKY

Fischer Streaky is a Real Antique Glass with one or more colors flashed in a streaked or patched pattern on a clear or colored base glass. Fischer Streakies are known for including white Opal in the streaky or patched design. Many streakies are dynamic and active, flowing in a roughly parallel, yet still irregular pattern, while others can be quiet and subtle. Each sheet of Fischer Streaky is a unique work of art that has been created individually by an experienced and dedicated team of glassblowers. No two sheets are exactly the same. Fischer Streakies can be used in their entirety in a door, window or lighting application.

FISCHER GLASS TYPES

FA-336 White on Blue

ENAMEL

Enamel glass is a smooth surfaced glass with no seeds or striation lines, similar to Goethe glass. However, unlike Goethe glass, a thick, uniform layer of milky white Opak is flashed on a base glass giving it an enamel appearance. Enamel glass are available in a variety of pastel colors. Fischer Enamel was specifically created for use in ultra-modern and contemporary living spaces.

FA-X350 Experimental Streaky

FA-X350 Experimental Streaky

EXPERIMENTAL STREAKY

Experimental Streakies are the positive results of continued research and development of new colors and combinations of colors carried out by A.C. Fischer. Each sheet is truly unique and cannot be adequately described in a few words. These streakies range from very active and dynamic to very quiet and refined. Some are solid opal streakies, others are transparent, "stringy" streakies. They are available in a great variety of colors and patterns.

FA-Blank

BLANK GLASS

Blank glass is a Real Antique Glass with striation lines and without seeds. Striation lines are small, irregular lines in the surface of the glass.

Cut Glass Cylinders Ready for Reheating and Flattening at 1200°F

C&R LOO, INC. WOULD LIKE TO THANK ALL OF THE PEOPLE WHO PARTICIPATED IN THIS PUBLICATION. TO INQUIRE ABOUT PARTICIPATING IN FUTURE PUBLICATIONS, QUANTITY DISCOUNT SALES OF THIS BOOK, OR FOR MORE INFORMATION ON A.C. FISCHER OR C&R LOO, PLEASE CONTACT US AT ONE OF THE ADDRESSES LISTED BELOW.

C&R LOO, INC.

1085 ESSEX AVENUE
RICHMOND, CA 94801
USA
(510) 232-0276 PHONE
(510) 232-7810 FAX

C&R LOO, GmbH

OLPENER STRAßE 321-323
D-51109 KÖLN
GERMANY
(0221) 89-10-71 PHONE
(0221) 89-10-74 FAX

FRANZ-LISZT-STRAßE 20
D-98529 SUHL
GERMANY
(03681) 28397 PHONE
(03681) 28397 FAX

LEUTKIRCHER STRAßE 20
D-88459 TANNHEIM
GERMANY
(08395) 7073 PHONE
(08395) 7634 FAX

LUGAR DEL PINERO 69, SANTA LUCIA
E-15893 SANTIAGO DE COMPOSTELLA
SPAIN
(34) 81549342 PHONE

A.C. FISCHER GLASHÜTTE BRAMSCHE GmbH

D-49565 BRAMSCHE
HAFENSTRAßE 9-13
GERMANY
(05461) 6912 PHONE
(05461) 4669 FAX

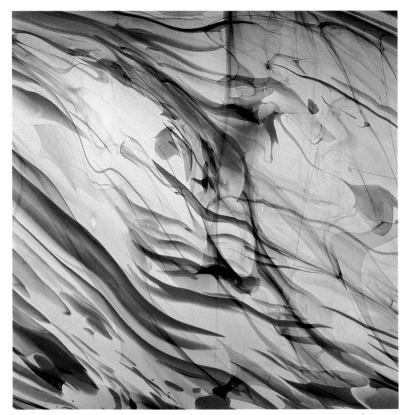

FA-383A Gold Pink Streaky